HOGS 'N' DOGS 'N' SLUGS 'N' BUGS

Collected Creature Poems

by

Nick Toczek

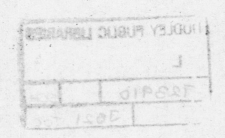
HOGS 'N' DOGS 'N' SLUGS 'N' BUGS

Contents

I'm A Slug 1

The Deadly Rattlesnake 2

Seasick 4

Where Sid The Spider Hid 5

Abominable Poem 7

Newt 8

Batley The Bat 9

Don't Do It 11

Pig Ahoy! 12

The Great Escape 13

How To Get A Fox Into A Matchbox 15

The Patient Lynx 17

Beast 18

Rat In The Attic 19

Dunk The Skunk 20

Danger-Spots 21

Getting A Goldfish 22

Beware Of The Dog 23

Prime Minister Pelican 24

The Pet Fanatic 26

While You're Asleep 28

Ted The Gorilla 30

Don't Marry Your Horse 31

The Slothful Ocelot 33

The End Of The Line-oh 34

The Unicorn 36

How The Bumble Bee Got His Stripes 37

A Turtle 40

The Day Our Teacher Brought Her Pet To School 41

Rhinos 43

The Dromedary 44

Choosing Some Suitable Pets 46

Giving The Pope An Antelope 47

When Buffaloes Buffle 49
The Little Olympics 50
Weird Wildlife 51
Mister Hannett And His Gannet .52
Never Stare At A Grizzly Bear 54
It's Sad About Sam 56
Greedy Cat 57
Freedom For Orang-utangs 59
Two Alphabet Zoos 60
A Cup Of Ale To Trap A Snail 61
Where Does That Dingo Go? 62
Once Bittern 64
When Elephants Dance On The Point Of A Pin 65
Peter The Cheetah 66
The Price Of Worms 67
The Ring-Tailed Lemur 68
The Turkey 69
Captain Goat And His Motorboat 71
Treating Chimps 72
Special Pets 73
Noggin-The-Nog 74
A Fuss About A Terrapin 75
A Palindrome For And Against Hunting 76
Broose, My Moose 77
The Strange Nun 78
Talkative Cows 79
The Tale Of A Snail 80
The Rabbit Who Tried To Catch The Moon 82
The Grice Mice Device 85
Cyril The Seafaring Squirrel 86
Fishy Tongue-Twisting Questions For The Sea-Slug 87

I'm A Slug

Sliding from my hiding-place
Somewhere damp and snug,
Steady as a river-barge
Or a harbour tug,
I glide across your garden
Chugga-chugga-chug,
Checking out the flowerbeds
That're freshly dug,
Chewing through new foliage...
Why? Cos I'm a slug.

A wet-weather voyager
On a silver rug,
Slimier than anything
Anyone would hug,
A black leather-jacketed
Shaven-headed thug,
Big baddie of the borders,
Worse than any bug,
I vandalise your veg-patch ...
Why? Cos I'm a slug.

You haven't put down pellets,
That's why I'm so smug.
Your plants are unprotected.
Here I come, you mug.
Although I know I'm stealing,
I'm not in a fug.
If I had any shoulders,
I would merely shrug.
You can't get *me* arrested ...
Why? Cos I'm a slug.

The Deadly Rattlesnake

Thin as a rake
A rattlesnake
Beneath a rock
Beside a lake
Begins to wake
Before daybreak
And gives its tail
A noisy shake.

An empty ache
Informs the snake
That it now has
A move to make,
A fast to break
And no mistake.
It gives its tail
A second shake.

Now wide awake
The rattlesnake
Uncoils itself...
A thirst to slake,
A meal to take;
Time to forsake
Its lonely lair
With one last shake.

And real, not fake,
This hungry snake
With poisoned fangs
For killing's sake
Would turn down cake.
It wants raw steak.
And creatures' hearts
Are right to quake.

Beware the deadly
rattlesnake!

Seasick

"I don't feel welk," whaled the squid, sole-fully.
"What's up?" asked the doctopus.
"I've got sore mussels and a tunny-hake," she told him.

"Lie down and I'll egg salmon you," mermaid the doctopus.
"Rays your voice," said the squid. "I'm a bit hard of herring."
"Sorry! I didn't do it on porpoise," replied the doctopus
orc-wardly.

He helped her to oyster self onto the couch
And asked her to look up so he could sea urchin,
He soon flounder plaice that hurt.

"This'll make it eel," he said, whiting a prescription.
"So I won't need to see the sturgeon?" she asked.
"Oh, no," he told her. "In a couple of dace you'll feel brill."

"Cod bless you," she said.
"That'll be sick squid," replied the doctopus.

Where Sid The Spider Hid

Sid the spider hid
Under the toilet lid.

He didn't! He did.
He didn't! He did.
I bet you a quid he did.
He didn't! He did.
He didn't! He did.
Under the toilet lid.
I kid you not, he did.

Sid the spider hid
This little arachnid
Who build his silky grid
Under the toilet lid.

He didn't! He did.
He didn't! He did.
I bet you a quid he did.
He didn't! He did.
He didn't! He did.
Under the toilet lid.
I kid you not, he did.

Sid the spider hid
But slipped one day and slid
We heard his eight feet skid
And bid goodbye to Sid
Then flushed the loo, we did
And so got rid of Sid
Who swam off like a squid.

He didn't! He did.
He didn't! He did.
I bet you a quid he did.
He didn't! He did.
He didn't! He did.
Under the toilet lid.
I kid you not, he did.

Abominable Poem

Tick-tock... tick-tock... tick-tock...
Mooooooooooooooo
BOOM!
That's a bomb in a bull.

Newt

It's better by far to own a newt
Than a bedbug or a bandicoot.
Truly, there's no substitute
For the ownership of a real live newt.

I'll tell you this: if I'd a newt
I'd feed it fish and free-range fruit,
French food freshly fried en croute,
Baked bean butties and boiled beetroot.

I'd dress my newt in a minute suit,
Shoving each claw in a Wellington boot,
And, every weekday, he'd commute
To a management job at an institute.

In war, my newt, as a raw recruit
Would learn to march and aim and shoot
And stand up straight and give a salute
And volunteer to execute
A daring raid by parachute.

And if life left me destitute,
My poverty utter and absolute...
Ah, well! I'd simply sell the brute
For a decent price cos he'd be a beaut

And you get a lotta loot
You get a lotta loot
You get a lotta loot
For a newt that's cute.

Batley The Bat

Between the rafters and the eaves
    Of the top-floor flat
In the house that wears its red roof
    Like a jaunty hat
Is the daytime dormitory
    Darkened habitat
Of Batley, the battered batty
    Acrobatic bat.

He has his high-pitched radar squeak
    But doesn't do chat,
Wears a coarse hair suit and pair of
    Wings for a cravat.
Ineloquent, inelegant,
    He's no diplomat.
He's Batley, the battered batty
    Acrobatic bat.

Jumpy as a startled rabbit
    Or a frightened cat,
He zigzags through the evening air
    Over where we're sat
Till we don't nextly know where he
    Will or won't be at.
He's Batley, the battered batty
    Acrobatic bat.

This insecure insectivore
    Who's more mouse than rat
Feeds and fattens himself up on
    Moth and midge and gnat,
Never eating crickets, though, cos
    He's no cricket bat.
He's Batley, the battered batty
    Acrobatic bat.

Don't Do It

It's really not very sens-erbil
To try to converse with your gerbil.
At language, the beast is terr-erbil.
At best, it'll utter a berbil,
A mutter a mite miser-erbil
That's wholly incomprehens-erbil.
So don't try to chat to your gerbil.
The creature's completely non-verbil.

Pig Ahoy!

Early one morning, a burly young pig,
Bright sailor-suited in waterproof rig,
Picnic snacks packed in a thingamajig,
Went and set sail on a fisherhog's brig.

Storm waves that day, though, grew surly and big.
Huge ones which each wore a curly white wig
Danced the poor boat in a desperate jig,
Chewing it up as if eating a fig,

Spitting out pieces the size of a twig.
Thirsty from this work, the sea took a swig,
Swallowing picnic and swallowing pig,
Easy as breathing in smoke from a cig.

The Great Escape

In the Great Escape from London Zoo
Eight caribou and gnu they knew
Mounted a minor military coup,
An act of animal derring-do,
And locked the staff they overthrew
In the 'potamus pit and a portaloo,
Then caught a plane to North Peru.

As animals broke out two-by-two
To squeal and growl and grunt and moo
A loud unruly queue soon grew
That wriggled and ran and crawled and flew,
Stampeding down the avenue.

In the Great Escape from London Zoo
We heard how the herd of kangaroo
Had bid the big brown owl adieu
with a: "Toodle-oo, mate, toodle-oo!"
But before he'd time to twit-tu-woo
They'd hopped it, heading for Timbuktu,
And the owl himself had flown off too.

While a crocodile and a cockatoo
Crossed the Thames in a slim canoe,
Rowed by the bird so the croc could chew...
Chew through the bones of the eight-man crew
Till the river ran red instead of blue.

In the Great Escape from London Zoo
The pandas abandoned their bamboo
And, all dressed up as railway crew,
Hi-jacked the fifteen fifty-two
From platform three at Waterloo
And, "parley-voo", they zoomed straight through
Paris, and on to Kathmandu.

Panic ensued and ballyhoo
When pot-bellied pig and rare-breed ewe
Gate-crashed a very posh barbecue
Terribly upsetting the well-to-do
And causing a heck of a hullabaloo.

You doubt my word? What's wrong with you?
Why, every detail here is true.
The Great Escape from London Zoo.
When was that? I thought you knew:
Years ago, at half-past two.

How To Get A Fox
Into A Matchbox

You'll need one fox
And one matchbox.
Undress your fox,
Remove its smocks,
Its skirts or frocks,
Its shirts, its jocks,
Its shoes and socks.
Then trim its locks.

Then slim your fox.
First hide its chocs;
Then make your fox,
While timed by clocks,
Swim lakes and lochs
And lift large rocks
And fight an ox
And run round blocks.

Then fool your fox.
Claim – shock of shocks –
That your matchbox
Contains its chocs
And hens in flocks
Plus plump peacocks
And crates and crocks
Of foxfood stocks.

Unorthodox?
A paradox?
So what? A pox
On he who mocks
Or carps or knocks
Cos... Bless my socks!
There's now a fox
In my matchbox.

Note: *unorthodox* means not normal and *a paradox* is something that seems
impossible or ridiculous.

The Patient Lynx

The day's been hot. A patient lynx
Lies in the long grass, waits, and thynx
Of waters lapping mud-bank brynx
Of pools, as heat-haze cools and shrynx.

Away to west, a slow sun synx,
Its blood-red circle spilling pynx
Into the blue and purple ynx
Of evening sky where one star twynx.

Late shadows lengthen round the lynx.
At last, it lifts its head and blynx.
Then, cautiously, the creature slynx
To water's edge and, watchful, drynx.

Beast

Doyen of the dead night. Silent goth.
Bullet-bodied babe of light-lured wrath.
A spell-born grub-spawn of witchcraft broth.

Papery wings of powdery cloth
Dyed the dark hues of the cauldron's froth.
Shadow of a butterfly. Fluttering moth.

Rat In The Attic

Rat-a-tat-tat. Rat-a-tat-tat.
Rat up in the attic. Oh, listen to that,
Rattling round like an acrobat,
That pitter-pattering, clattering rat.

Rat-a-tat-tat. Rat-a-tat-tat.
We can't sleep. Here we're sat.
Never heard anything quite like that,
That pitter-pattering, clattering rat.

Rat-a-tat-tat. Rat-a-tat-tat.
Drat that brat! Cut the chat.
Catch that prat to feed the cat,
That pitter-pattering, clattering rat.

Rat-a-tat-tat. Rat-a-tat-tat.
Flatten that rat. Batter the brat!
Splatter that un-get-at-able rat!
That pitter-pattering, clattering rat.

Rat-a-tat-tat. Rat-a-tat-tat.
Crush that rat cowpat flat.
One quick splat with a cricket bat.
That pitter-pattering, clattering rat.

Rat-a-tat-tat. Rat-a-tat-tat.
Rat up in the attic. Will you listen to that?
Rat-a-tat-tat. Rat-a-tat-tat.
Rat-a-tat-tat. Rat-a-tat-tat.
Rat-a-tat-tat. Rat-a-tat-tat.

Dunk The Skunk

No-one wanted to play with Duncan.
He was a black-'n'-white furry skunk 'n'
He'd got a home with a chair and bunk 'n'
It was in a hole in an old tree-trunk 'n'
It smelt worse that an unwashed punk 'n'
Dunc fell out of it with a KER-PLUNK! 'n'
Hit a heap of twigs and woodland junk 'n'
Raised his tail and squirted gunk 'n'
Everybody said how much it stunk 'n'
Turned their backs and away they slunk 'n'
No one wanted to play with Duncan.

Danger-Spots

When in a country
With a climate
More than tepid-y

A jungle walk
Is well and good
If you're intrepid-y

Or in a party
Safely led
By someone shepherd-y

But should you spot
A spotted cat
Whose pelt is peppered-y

A large and loping
Streamlined feline
Looking leopard-y

That's heading your way
Relocate yourself
Quick-stepper-dy

Because to stay there's
To remain where
You're in jeopardy.

Getting A Goldfish

We bought ourselves a goldfish
From a Polish man who sold fish.
It's a very cold-to-hold fish
On slow patrol
Around round its bowl.
I'm told it's quite an old fish.

Beware Of The Dog

Bang on the door
Bang on the door
Bang on the door of sixty-four
But don't ignore their Labrador
Who'll give your leg a nasty gnaw
And leave it bleeding, red and raw
And terribly, terribly, terribly sore
And that's because a Labrador
Is naturally a carnivore.

Bang on the door
Bang on the door
Bang on the door of sixty-four
So long as you're sure you know the score
And not before, no, not before
You're well aware of what's in store.
Look at the jaw. Look at the paw.
Size of the tooth, size of the claw
And that's because a Labrador
Is naturally a carnivore.

Bang on the door
Bang on the door
Bang on the door of sixty-four...
If you dare!

Prime Minister Pelican

Prime Minister pelican
Is pictured in the street
With his self-important waddle
And his aura of conceit,

A plumply pompous personage
Composed of poultry-meat
Who tops the pecking-order
Of the ruling-class elite.

There's something of the suit about him,
Leather-booted feet,
Big belly built by banqueting,
Big beak that's obsolete.

He's flown into the city
From his parliamentary seat.
Election-time is looming.
There are rumours of defeat.

The talk in all the tabloids
Is that he's been indiscrete,
So he's got lots of work to do
And creatures he's to meet.

And then there'll be a speech to make
That's riddled with deceit.
The way to stay in power
When you're losing is to cheat.

In better times he'd hide himself
Some distance from this heat
Away from all these cameras
In his countryside retreat.

But politics is perilous.
Its prize is bittersweet.
And so he's faked a gracious grin
And gone outside to greet

The media; this pelican
Who's posing in the street,
His body oddly dignified,
Ridiculous but neat.

The Pet Fanatic

Every morning, you awake
With cattle in your bed and a rattlesnake.
You take a dip in your swimming pool
With your hippopotamus and your mule,
Then you have breakfast on your lawn
In the company of a coastal prawn,
Before you fly off in your jet
To work in the city with your marmoset.

From your office, you email
Letters of love to your favourite snail.
After that, you share a cab
With a vampire bat and a hermit crab.
Soon you're strolling through the park
Chatting with a vole and an old aardvark,
Or riding high in a horse-drawn coach,
Sat by the side of a large cockroach.

For lunch, you go to cocktail bars
Drinking punch with jaguars and a bunch of drunk
tarantulas.
At your club, you then play bridge
With two chipmunks and a moody midge.
Next, you go to a fashion show
With forty crows and a water buffalo.
At half-past-three, you take high tea
With a fly and a flea and a bumble bee.

Then, perhaps, to a picture-house
Watching a movie, sat with a mouse
Having hot popcorn and a laugh
With a film-fan fawn and a pedigree giraffe.
(Not to a play, cos plot and drama
Bore your ocelot and your llama).
On to a restaurant, sharing courses
With a portly pig and a pair of shire horses.

On the bus, you sit and discuss
Literature with an octopus.
Home at last and up the stairs,
You call goodnight to your grizzly bears
And to all your other teds
Who've said their prayers and are in their beds.
"Lights out!" shouts the armadillo.
Your head has hardly hit the pillow
But the room has filled with counted sheep
And you're already fast asleep.

While You're Asleep

Under the stars that all stand still
Whole herds of clouds gallop silently across a buttered moon.
They wake no-one. Their hard hooves
Have been hushed in cushions of cotton wool.

Round the guttered rooftops far below
Lie the long and looping flight-paths
Down which black bats flutter, pig-nosed
With wings like leather umbrellas.

Beneath these moth-fed squadrons of night-mice
And all bagged up in blackness,
Our garden pond ripples
As softly as a baby snoring.

The bulging belly-button of this pond
Is the flat head of the fat frog
Who crouches with his body
And his bent legs buried below the surface.

And what does our frog-friend do all night?
Not much. He just sits
Gulping down dollops of dark air
As if chewing chunks of chocolate.

Oh, but he's so comfy out there,
Caught in the cool cuddle of his cot of water
Where the small dreams of smooth newts
Wrap right round him like a smoky blanket.

What might we find inside these tiny sleeping minds?
Shadows of the long-gone day.
Pond memories pulled, like lifted toads from this muddled
   mud.
Perhaps the sudden sight of a dragonfly, sunlit,
Seen flitting by, bright as a sparkler.
Or else echoes of small-talk
Buzzed by the silly milling teatime crowds
Of midges dancing a tangled tango above the pool.

Don't wake. The new day is miles away.

Ted The Gorilla

Old Ted, the gorilla,
His head on his pillow,
Got iller and iller and iller.

Old Ted, the gorilla,
Though fed a germ-killer,
Got iller and iller and iller.

Old Ted, the gorilla,
His voice getting shriller,
Got iller and iller and iller.

Old Ted, the gorilla,
Though still a pill-swiller,
Got iller and iller and iller.

Old Ted, the gorilla,
Lay dead on his pillow
And never got iller
Or stilled or chiller,
No, never got iller than that!

Don't Marry Your Horse

Whatever you do, dear,
Don't marry that horse.
I've heard from a very reliable source
That life in a stable
Is vulgar and coarse.

And, anyway, how
Could you marry a horse
Who'd have you drink water
And eat grass and gorse
With no meat-'n'-gravy
Or horseradish sauce?

The multiple drawbacks
Of marriage to horse
Have occupied many
A learned discourse
In Latin and Hebrew
And Urdu and Norse.

And I've told and cajoled you
To not wed said horse.
It's a union no one
I know would endorse.
Now I'm blue in the face
And my voice has grown hoarse.

And yet you're insisting
You'll marry your horse.
It'll end in a mess of
Regret and remorse.
How can I dissuade you
From taking this course?

My sweet, I implore you,
Don't marry that horse.
I'm sure there's a law
That the courts can enforce
To stop it and spare you
The pain of divorce.

You can find something better
To wed than a horse.
I'll tap it out, letter
By letter, in Morse:
Don't marry, don't marry,
Don't marry that horse.

The Slothful Ocelot

Shunning life's chaos a lot
An ocelot'll doss a lot
Will lie and gather moss a lot,
Its brain like candy-floss a lot.
Its lazy legs'll cross a lot
As if it was our boss a lot.

It treats us all like dross a lot
And makes us all get cross a lot,
But doesn't give a toss a lot
Which leaves us at a loss a lot.
That's why we're glad an ocelot's
Not what we come across a lot.

The End Of The Line-oh

A rhino
That I know
With a flair
For design-oh
Had his cage
Lined with lino
And polished it daily
To maintain its shine-oh.

He showed it to me
And declared it so fine-oh
A king or a queen could
Sit down there and dine-oh.
But, sadly, last week,
Having drunk too much wine-oh,
He slipped there and tripped there
And snapped his poor spine-oh.

He couldn't get up
So we called nine-nine-nine-oh.
In hospital, though,
He went into decline-oh
And died. Well we've lain him
In a casket of pine-oh
And lined it, for the rhino,
With polished black lino.

We pay our respects to him
Here in this shrine-oh
Where he seems at peace
In the sleep that's divine-oh
While, softly, the choristers
Sing *Auld Lang Syne*-oh.
And is there an eye
In this church that is dry? No.

The Unicorn

While in a pub in Ballythorn
I met a man whose name was Shawn.
He said, as sure as he was born,
His white horse had a single horn
And wings, although I could have sworn
He winked and glanced at me with scorn
When I said: "That's a unicorn!
Now tell me more." He'd not be drawn.
I bought him pints of Old Acorn.
It didn't help. He gave a yawn,
Said: "Visit me tomorrow morn
-ing. I got up at crack of dawn
To go to see that unicorn.
Shawn led me there, but looked forlorn,
His face all sad, his eyes care-worn.
He showed me hoof-marks on the lawn
And half a tether which was torn.
He said: "You've missed my unicorn.
I tied it here, but now it's gorn."

How The Bumble Bee
Got His Stripes

On the day that the world began,
Each of the creatures was shown
Every colour in the universe;
And all were told to choose
Which of these they wanted for themselves.

Well, that day the elephant
Thought carefully and chose to be grey,
But the bumble bee
Just bumbled around and buzzed around
And couldn't make up his mind,
And the yellow sun shone so brightly
That the bumble bee's bum became yellow.

And that night the goldfish
Thought carefully and chose to be golden,
But the bumble bee
Just bumbled around and buzzed around
And couldn't make up his mind,
And the black night grew so dark
That the bumble bee's hips became black.

And next day the cricket
Thought carefully and chose to be green,
But the bumble bee
Just bumbled around and buzzed around
And couldn't make up his mind,
And the yellow sun shone so brightly
That the bumble bee's waist became yellow.

And that night the owl
Thought carefully and chose to be brown,
But the bumble bee
Just bumbled around and buzzed around
And couldn't make up his mind,
And the black night grew so dark
That the bumble bee's chest became black.

And next day the polar bear
Thought carefully and chose to be white,
But the bumble bee
Just bumbled around and buzzed around
And couldn't make up his mind,
And the yellow sun shone so brightly
That the bumble bee's shoulders became yellow.

And that night the jay
Thought carefully and chose to be blue,
But the bumble bee
Just bumbled around and buzzed around
And couldn't make up his mind,
And the black night grew so dark
That the bumble bee's neck and head and legs
became black.

And next day the bumble bee
Began to be thoughtful.
He bumbled around and buzzed around
But thought carefully,
And chose the colours he wanted to be.
He said: "I've made up my mind.
I want to be all the colours of the rainbow."
But it was too late
Because the bumble bee
Had already become black striped
And yellow striped,
From the top of his head
To the tips of his toes.

A Turtle

Imagine a turtle
Named Mi-shell or Murtle.

Ashore she should surely
Creep lowly, crawl slowly.

Were you to turn turtle
You'd not soar or hurtle.

When you then grew furtle
As that female turtle,

You'd crawl up a beach
On your plump, stumpy legs,

Dig deep in the dirt
And deposit your eggs.

A turtle expurtle
Know you'll need no nest.

Your clutch'll do best
Where you've laid it to rest.

Who'll hide, heat and hatch it?
The durtle.

The Day Our Teacher Brought Her Pet To School

Oh, that was a day that we'll never forget,
And one our poor teacher will always regret.
What set our whole class in a terrible sweat
Was the creature that teacher described as her pet.

At lunchtime that day in the infants' toilet,
They found what was left of a smoked cigarette.
The head blamed a pupil, but it's a safe bet
That the one who had done it was our teacher's pet.

It challenged us all to a game of roulette –
Won our dinner money. We've not eaten yet.
And each of the teachers is deeply in debt
To the champion gambler that's our teacher's pet.

The caretaker chased it around with a net
Till it was as angry as animals get.
Then, down in the playground, the two of them met
And the human got eaten by our teacher's pet.

They say music's soothing when beasts are upset,
But this one found most tunes a bit of a threat.
There wasn't much left of the school string quartet
When they played Beethoven to our teacher's pet.

It chewed through three children who played clarinet
But, while it was dining on a drum majorette,
We lowered a noose from a high parapet,
Thereby roping and capturing our teacher's pet.

We took it to be put down by our local vet;
But it ate him, a parrot, a pet marmoset,
A beagle, a budgie, an ailing egret,
And a litter of kittens, did our teacher's pet.

The details appeared in The Evening Gazette.
Later that night though, an air force cadet
At the RAF base saw a dark silhouette
Of a shape somewhat similar to our teacher's pet.

At midnight, our school was bombed flat by a jet,
Reduced to mere rubble by one Exocet.
The head blamed a terrorist gang from Tibet,
But all of us knew it was our teacher's pet.

Rhinos

At the zoo we saw a rhinoceros
And a second rhinoceros too...
Or a second rhino saw us too.
And it's due either to the rhinos or us
That we can't now be sure
Just how many we saw
Nor how many rhinos saw us.

The Dromedary

A camel's enamel's
Like some dental dump,
Each tooth an irregular
Yellowing stump.
This gobful in total
Is one ugly clump.

From the Mick Jagger lips
Of this pouting grump
Come both breath and voice
That resemble a trump,
And jets of its spittle
When it's got the hump...

Which sits on its back
Between shoulders and rump.
This fatty protuberant
Over-large lump
Makes even slim dromedaries
Seem somewhat plump.

Flat feet like four mop-heads.
Pray pity the chump.
Inelegant creature,
It can't jive or jump,
Just jog along awkwardly –
Thumpity-thump.

Head held high and back up
But neck in a slump,
No wonder the camel
Appears such a frump
Going bumpity bumpity
Bump bump-bump.

Note: *got the hump* is slang for upset or angry.

Choosing Some Suitable Pets

Big bugs and fat slugs
And blood-sucking leeches:
Things that come wriggling
From plump plums and peaches;

Growlers and howlers
And screamers and screechers;
Vile-bodied vermin
With foulest of features;

Rubbery, blubbery
Deep-water species
Of sea-beasts whose bodies
Get washed up on beaches;

Appalling things crawling
From damp nooks and niches;
Slimy life climbing
Where light never reaches;

Hair-nits and hornets;
The grubs of such creatures...
It's hard to choose which pets
To give to your teachers.

Giving The Pope
An Antelope

How do you cope?
How do you cope?
How do you cope
With an antelope?

It's not quite bright
But a big dumb dope
That'll impolitely
Grab and grope.

I can't cope
I can't cope
I can't cope
With my antelope.

It'll lazily graze
On a grassy slope
Or gaze for days
Down my telescope.

I raised my problem
With the Pope
Who praised its wobbling
Awkward lope.

He could cope.
He could cope.
He could cope
With an antelope.

I scrubbed mine down
In bubbly soap,
Tugged it around
On a length of rope,

Took it to the Vatican.
When the Pope
Said "Take it back again!"
I said: "Nope.
You're my last hope.

I know you'll cope.
I know you'll cope.
I know you'll cope
With my antelope.

When Buffaloes Buffle

When watching wild buffaloes buffle
Observe their uncomfortable shuffle.
It's winter. You're warm in your duffel-
Coat, thick woollen gloves and your muffle.

It's snowful where buffaloes buffle
So note how they woefully whuffle
And snotfully sniffle and snuffle
Like pigs in pursuit of a truffle.

Don't buffet a buffalo's buffle.
The big beast is easy to ruffle.
Beware. The ensuing rough stuff'll
Cause suffering during the scuffle.

And a buffalo's baffling buffle
When it's interrupted enough'll
Erupt into such a kerfuffle
Your bones'll receive a reshuffle.

The Little Olympics

When fleas bite your ankles
Their leaping skill rankles
Despite all their neat somersaulting;
But when you've a fleabite
At neck, chest or knee height,
It means that the beasts are pole-vaulting.

Weird Wildlife

It's a queer cat
Is the meerkat.
It cannot purr or meow.
And how odd-ish
That no dogfish
Knows how to bow-wow-wow.

The ladybird
Is seldom heard
To tweet, and never sings.
And that wombat's
Too round and fat
To be a mouse with wings.

There are no ants
Like eleph ants,
None even near their size.
And guinea pigs
Aren't mini pigs
And don't inhabit sties

While the mongoose
Is a wrong goose.
You'll seldom see one fly.
And bushbabies
Are hushed babies
That hardly ever cry.

Mister Hannett And His Gannet

(for Bradford school teacher, Bob Hannett)

Mister Hannett bought a gannet
from an aviary in Thanet
but the city council sanit-
ation people tried to ban it.

Through the post to Mister Hannett
went a letter headed: Sanit-
ation Central Office an' it
came straight from the man who ran it.

Here is how the man began it:
"Mister Hannett, re your gannett
ownership, we feel you cannot..."
and the rest was self-explanat-

ory. Bureaucratic insanit-
y would take away the gannet.
Mister Hannett, face like granite,
showed his letter to the janit-

Or and let the old man scan it
whose head was like a pomegranate.
Unbeknown to Mister Hannett,
his friend was from another planet.

Astronomically uncanny t-
wists of fate and Mister Hannett
seldom meet, but actually can at
times when moon aligns with planet.

Life, there's nothing stranger than it.
So it was an interplanet-
ary spaceship with, to man it,
men with heads like pomegranate-

s came to visit Mister Hannett.
Now the council simply cannot
Part the teacher from his gannett.
Both live on another planet.

Never Stare At A Grizzly Bear

You can stand and stare at a teddy bear,
Glower and glare without a care;
But it's only fair to make you aware
That a grizzly bear is a different affair.

Yes, a grizzly bear is a different affair.
Friendly ones are fairly rare.
Believe me, then, when I declare
If you bump into one on the thoroughfare
Or happen to stray into its lair
Or trap it in a pit or a similar snare
Or it eats your porridge and breaks your chair,
All I can say is you'd better beware.
Prepare yourself for a scary affair
That'll probably turn out a proper nightmare.
And it only takes one careless stare.

It only takes one careless stare
To make it mad and drive it spare
Cos a bear can't bear a human stare.
And the worst of these is the grizzly bear
With claws that rip and slash and tear.
That's the grizzly truth, the grizzly truth,
The grizzly truth, I swear.

For your own welfare, best gaze elsewhere,
Like over here or over there,
Directly down at your leather footwear
Or up at the weather in the wind-blown air;
But never ever stare, no never ever stare,
Don't dare to stare at a grizzly bear
Cos a bear can't bear a human stare,
And worst of all is the grizzly bear.

It snorts and snarls. Its nostrils flare.
You haven't got a hope. You're beyond despair
Cos, before you've time to say a prayer,
It'll chew through you, chew through you,
Chew through you like a chocolate éclair.

Chew through you like a chocolate éclair,
Till you're just bare bones... and your underwear.

It's Sad About Sam

Sam got chased by the farmer's cow.
He climbed the old oak tree somehow
But tumbled head-first from that bough
And landed on the farmer's sow.

This started up a dreadful row,
The kind that no one should allow,
With squealing pig, while Sam yelled "OW!"
The cat went: "MIAOW!" The dog: "BOW-WOW!"

The farmer swung a punch: KER-POW!
His fist hit Sam square on his brow
Which knocked him backwards on the plough
So poor old Sam is mincemeat now.

Greedy Cat

Our cat, hollow as a hat,
Gobbled up a string-tailed rat
And the whole of a bowl of cooking fat.

So what do you think of that, then?
What do you think of that?

Our cat, hollow as a hat,
Gobbled up a string-tailed rat,
The whole of a bowl of cooking fat,
A sturgeon, a stickleback, a sea sprat
And a pig-nosed, leather-winged vampire bat.

So what do you think of that, then?
What do you think of that?

Our cat, hollow as a hat,
Gobbled up a string-tailed rat,
The whole of a bowl of cooking fat,
A sturgeon, a stickleback, a South Sea sprat,
A pig-nosed, leather-winged vampire bat,
A starling, a redstart, a dead stonechat,
A big bluebottle and a tiny gnat.

So what do you think of that, then?
What do you think of that?

Our cat, hollow as a hat,
Gobbled up a string-tailed rat,
The whole of a bowl of cooking fat,
A sturgeon, a stickleback, a South Sea sprat,
A pig-nosed, leather-winged vampire bat,
A starling, a redstart, a dead stonechat,
A big bluebottle, a tiny gnat,
A mango, a paw-paw, a ripe kumquat
And the next-door neighbour's pet wombat.

So what do you think of that, then?
What do you think of that?

Our cat, hollow as a hat,
Gobbled up a string-tailed rat,
The whole of a bowl of cooking fat,
A sturgeon, stickleback, South Sea sprat,
A pig-nosed, leather-winged vampire bat,
A starling, a redstart, a dead stonechat,
A big bluebottle, a tiny gnat,
A mango, a paw-paw, a ripe kumquat,
The next-door neighbour's pet wombat,
And a road-killed rabbit that was very, very,
Very, very, very, very, very, very, very, very flat.

So what do you think of that, then?
What do you think of that?

Freedom For Orang-utangs

Last week while the midnight church bell rang,
An animal liberation gang
Broke into the zoo and there they sprang
A Borneo-born orang-utang,
Luring the beast with lemon meringue.

But the keeper heard the cage-door clang,
Picked up his pistol and fired it: "Bang!"
Missed by a mile and hit a boomslang
Causing the serpent to lose a fang
And writhe and hiss. Well, it really stang.

The keeper then began to harangue
The thieves in words which were workman's slang
Each one of them worse than 'drat' or 'dang' –
Shocking expletives, the whole shebang,
And he swore for sure that gang would hang.

But, as they fled, they laughed and sang.
They felt no guilt, not a single pang,
Not a tiny twinge or twitch or twang,
As they sped off in their Ford Mustang
Free as a bird... or orang-utang.

Two Alphabet Zoos

1.

ABC: the water buffalee
DEF: the chimpanzeff
GHI: the anacondeye
JKL: the bird of paradell
MNO: the hippopotamo
PQR: the porcupar
STU: the butterflew
VW: the chameleoo
XYZ: the kangared

2.

ABC: the African elephanee
DEF: the wildebeff
GHI: the polar bye
JKL: the octopell
MNO: the spiney ant-eatoe
PQR: the rhinocerar
STU: the crocadoo
VW: the budgerigoo
XYZ: the tarantuled.

(N.B. If you're American and say 'zee' instead of 'zed', it'd be 'kangaree' and 'tarantulee')

A Cup Of Ale To Trap A Snail

We knew an ugly rugged snail
Whose underside was oddly pale,
His body small, but built to scale,
A rather self-regarding male
Whose name was Feathery Knight-in-Gale.

We wonder whether he...
Whether he... whether he...
Weather'll turn to hail.

He was a stout out-going snail,
A tiny walk-on-water whale
Who surfed a stream-like silver trail
On one fat foot, its boot hobnail,
That dragged a lazy leathery tail.

We wonder whether he...
Whether he... whether he...
Weather'll turn to hail.

Where is this kidney-coloured snail?
He slid into a cup of ale
And found he couldn't swim or sail
So tried to float... to no avail.
All together to end his tale:

We wonder whether he...
Whether he... whether he...
Weather'll turn to hail.

Where Does That Dingo Go?

No one knows where the dingo goes
Ahead of its tail, but behind its nose.

It must go somewhere, I suppose,
Though I know nobody who knows.
And so this problem first arose -
A mystery that no one chose.

No one knows where the dingo goes
Ahead of its tail, but behind its nose.

It breezes in but won't disclose
Quite where it's been before it shows,
Stays a while, then away it blows
With no goodbyes or cheerios.

No one knows where the dingo goes
Ahead of its tail, but behind its nose.

This dog doggedly tos and fros,
Says no yeses and says no noes
To all the questions which we pose.
Curiosity overflows!

No one knows where the dingo goes
Ahead of its tail, but behind its nose.

Though sleuths line up in rows and rows,
They're each knocked down like dominoes.
There's no detective can expose
Where dingo sneaks on tippy-toes.

No one knows where the dingo goes
Ahead of its tail, but behind its nose.

A case no Sherlock Holmes can close,
Nor would-be Maigrets or Clouseaus;
Or Father Browns, Hercule Poirots,
Or Scotland Yard, or all of those
Employed by Federal Bureaux.

No one knows where the dingo goes
Ahead of its tail, but behind its nose.

It's a riddle that grows and grows and grows.

Once Bittern

The double-bass boom of the bittern,
Once common across much of Britain,
Is now seldom heard.
This endangered bird's
As rare as a poem well-written.

When Elephants Dance
On The Point Of A Pin

When elephants twirl on the point of a pin,
They pirouette perfectly, pair up and spin
As if they were elegant, agile and thin,
Maintaining their motion with deft discipline,
Their graceful gyrations inducing a grin,
Each movement too magical to imagine,
But it's no illusion, it's quite genuine.
They're pachyderms, meaning they've all got thick skin
That's too tough for pressure to push that pin in.

When elephants waltz on the point of a pin,
They may choose to do so to tunes by Gershwin,
Or rich ragtime rhythms wrought by Scott Joplin,
Or jazzed up jive music by Irving Berlin,
Or maybe to bluegrass on mad mandolin,
Or folderol folk blown down whistles of tin
Or fiddled away on a fine violin
That's carefully cradled between head and chin
By someone as skilled as the great Menuhin.

When elephants prance on the point of a pin,
They hate interruptions, detest any din,
Demanding their audience meet that doctrine
By dumping their crisp packets into the bin
And switching off mobiles (each ringtone's a sin!)
And stifling sniffles at their origin
And calling off coughs with some strong medicine
And anyone talking is worse than vermin
So hush, everyone... They're about to begin...

Peter The Cheetah

Here's Peter the champion cheetah.

Well fed on the meat of
A freshly killed bleater,
That's Peter the champion cheetah.

No running-style's neater,
No pacing is sweeter.
It's Peter the champion cheetah.

Our fastest competer
At eight hundred metres
Is Peter the champion cheetah.

A race-goer's treat and
A loping lap-eater.
Yeah, Peter the champion cheetah.

A feline world-beater;
Few creatures are fleeter
Than Peter the champion...
Peter the champion...
Peter the champion cheetah.

The Price Of Worms

Well, what on earth
Is an earthworm worth?
Would you swap one worm
For a modicum of mirth,
For a third of a word,
Or a fourth of firth,

For a part of a port
To the north of Perth,
Or a nine-pence note,
Or a boat's best berth,
Or a fish-fur coat
Of enormous girth?

What if worms were rare?
What if there was a dearth
When a whole lot of earthworms
Died at birth?
Then perhaps one worm
Would cost The Earth.

The Ring-Tailed Lemur

That bone in your leg is a femur.
That pan on the hob is a steamer.
That atom bomb hit Hiroshima.

That stripy-tailed creature's a lemur.

That bloke behind bars is a schemer.
In slang my posh car is a 'Beamer'.
That island out there's Iwo Jima.

That masked Madagascan's a lemur.

That colourful ribbon's a streamer.
Peru's prima city is Lima
And when you're asleep, you're a dreamer.

That cute omnivore is a lemur.

I'll scare you and make you a screamer.
That prayer there is for your redeemer,
But swear and you'll be a blasphemer.

No squirrel or cat, that's a lemur.

The Turkey

Just how this odd bird has occurred
Can only be vaguely inferred.
Its history's a mystery
That's murky and blurred.
The turkey's a circus-freak sort of a bird
Like nothing else feathered or finned or furred
Found in a flock or a shoal or a herd.

This gobbledy-geek with a beak
Is simply absurdly unique.
It's more than just slightly
Ungainly, unsightly.
Not wrongly but rightly
– although impolitely –
It's known as a berk of a bird.

The creature's creator has erred.
Nature, summed up in a word,
Is a nerd for building the bird
To a plan gone berserk.
Its wings will not work.
Its body's ballooned.
Its head's been cartooned.
It's gawky. It's quirky.
It's awkwardly jerky.

It's turkey we're talking.
Just look how it's walking.
It's dozy. It's dorky.
It's portly-to-porky
And what squawky bird
Have you ever heard
With such an odd choice of a voice?

Captain Goat And
His Motorboat

This note I wrote
For you to quote
And learn by rote
Concerns a boat

A boat afloat
Upon a moat –
The motorboat
Of Captain Goat.

His motorboat
Had had a coat
A sealing coat
Of creosote.

Well, wood afloat
Will quickly bloat
But creosote's
The antidote

And so the goat
Had paid a groat
(That's next to nowt)
To Sailor Stoat

So he'd devote
At least a mote
Of time to coat
In creosote

That motorboat
So goat and stoat
Would stay afloat
Upon the moat.

Treating Chimps

Chimpanzeeses catch diseases
Such as sniffles, such as sneezes,
Such as coffles, such as wheezes.
Wrap 'em well when winter freezes.

Chimpanzeeses catch diseases
When they're left in drafts and breezes.
They get pain that grips and seizes.
Ease it all with hugs and squeezes.

Chimpanzeeses catch diseases,
Queasiness that nags and teases.
All the usual food displeases.
Feed them chick-peas, chives and cheeses.

Chimpanzeeses catch diseases,
Get uneases in their kneeses
From the bites of mites and fleases.
Pick these bugs out using tweezers.
Rub unsightly sores with greases.

These is ways we treats diseases
Which get caught by chimpanzeeses.

Special Pets

We're not like your budgie, your goldfish or puss.
No fur, fins or feathers. No growling or fuss.
Indeed, we're mild-mannered and quite courteous
So we'd like to thank you for caring for us,
For feeding and giving us comfortableness.

Our cousins are bugs. They inhabit your bed
And feed on your blood till they're fat, round and red;
While we are the family of lice on your head
Who don't want your blood, just your dandruff instead.

We're unlike the pets that you'd usually discuss.
And pet shops don't sell us, we're bad for business.
You've hundreds and thousands and millions of us.
You're our home and banquet, our playground and bus.
So thank you, most kindly, for caring for us.

Noggin-The-Nog

Meet our dog: Noggin-the-Nog,
Probably the world's most ancient dog.

He's blind as a bat, with eyes like fog,
Lies in the lane like a fallen log,
With a brain dad says has lost a cog
And a bark that's like a strangled frog.

Noggin-the-Nog, Noggin-the-Nog,
Probably the world's most ancient dog.

He's chewed up the Argos catalogue,
Mum's slipper, my shoe and grandad's clog.
He waits for the postman, all agog,
Then sees him off at a jaunty jog.

Noggin-the-Nog, Noggin-the-Nog,
Probably the world's most ancient dog.

Living with him is a thankless slog.
He's more grumpy than an old hedgehog
And smells like The Beast from Bodmin Bog;
Not the sort of dog that pet shops flog.

Noggin-the-Nog, Noggin-the-Nog,
Probably the world's most ancient dog.

A Fuss About A Terrapin

I've lots of questions. Let's begin...
Why's it got such crumpled skin?
Is that a flipper, leg or fin?
Where's its ankle, knee or shin?

You just can't tell
You just can't tell
You just can't tell with a terrapin.

Why's it silent? Why no din?
Is this monastic discipline?
Or punishment for some past sin?
Is that a grimace or a grin?

You just can't tell
You just can't tell
You just can't tell with a terrapin.

Could that shell lift like lid of bin?
Or would it open like a tin?
And what's the body like within?
Is it fat or is it thin?

You just can't tell
You just can't tell
You just can't tell with a terrapin.

Is that head partly out or in?
Where does the neck become a chin?
Would turtles be its next of kin
Or tortoises...? Oh I give in!

You just can't tell
You just can't tell
You just can't tell with a terrapin.

A Palindrome For And Against Hunting

Evil won.
We footstep on bats,
Trap a wolf,
Stun deer,
Gas rats.
O! Slay anon!

No!
Nay also!
Stars agreed: "Nuts!"
Flow apart. Stab no pets,
Too few now live.

Broose, My Moose

I caught a moose
And called him Broose.
I tied him with a few lassoose
Securely to a towering sproose.

I groomed my moose
With grease of goose
And soaps and scents the French prodoose
And oily inks of octopoose.

I loved that moose.
What was the yoose?
He ate my meals, he drank my joose,
But gave back only moose aboose.

Can you dedoose
Quite why my moose
Was so ungrateful and obtoose?
Perhaps he was a few scroose loose.

I'd introdoose
You all to Broose,
But can't do so cos he broke loose
By chewing through each ropy noose.

Don't ask why Broose
Chose to vamoose.
He gave no reason or excoose.

Perhaps I'd caught the wrong moose.
Next time, I'll get a mongoose.

The Strange Nun

A nun at the zoo in Berlin
Surprised me when she said she'd been
Hatched out of an egg.
"You're pulling my leg!"
"I'm not," she said. "I'm a penguin."

Talkative Cows

Have you heard the tittle-tattle
From a chatty herd of cattle?

Chewing cud and chewing fat'll
Set the tongues of cows a-rattle.

Each'll natter, each'll prattle,
Chatter like a diplomat'll.

When they row, there's little that'll
End their bitter verbal battle.

So, if you can hush these cattle,
I'll not only eat my hat, I'll
Swim from Scarborough to Seattle!

The Tale Of A Snail

I bring you a tale about a snail
Who's hardy, healthy, hearty and hale,
A hunky and chunky meaty male
The shape and shade of a Minke whale
Without a waterspout or tail
And made on a much more minute scale,
Body the breadth of my big toenail
But a macho snail in each detail.

His broad back's leathered and rough as braille
And bears a shell that's weathered and frail.
Although his underside's soft and pale,
He's fit for a fight, hard as a nail,
Tough as old ropes to haul up a sail
And strong as a farmhouse Wensleydale.
He knows of no hillside he'll not scale
Nor a cliff down which he'll not abseil.

No sickness succeeds to make him ail
And viruses vie to no avail
Within the fine physique of this snail
Whose butch beefy body's sans pareille.
This most magnificent mollusc male
Who'd boldly battle both frost and hail,
Take on a downpour, tackle a gale,
Though he's heroic, is doomed to fail...

For he's fallen for a fellow snail,
Slavishly follows the silver trail
Of a gorgeous gastropod female,
A beguiling beast named Abigail.
Well, he's wooed his girl with curly kale
And lettuce leaves which he stole wholesale
From allotments, rashly risking jail
Entailing years without hope of bail.

His problem, though, is a rival snail,
A second and slimy male called Dale,
Slippery, slithery, fond of ale,
Who's taken a shine to Abigail.
Cupid's cruel arrow thus finds twin male
Hearts to impale, so turning love stale.
When two pursue the same Holy Grail
The booze they brew's a potent cocktail.

For those stolen leaves, Dale tries blackmail,
Demanding money and Abigail.
Then when he's refused, he turns telltale
Secretly sending by sly snail-mail
Letters revealing in dark detail
The theft of lettuce and curly kale.
As cops get onto our hero's trail,
Dastardly Dale prepares to prevail.

Now our wanted hero vows that they'll
Not take him before he's dealt with Dale.
While cop cars prowl and their sirens wail,
The two snails meet on a path of shale.
They clash. Shells crash. They thrash and flail...
But are squashed beneath the hard hobnail
Boot of hiker en route to Wales.

The Rabbit Who Tried To Catch The Moon

I've served, since young, as a dragoon
And seen the world with my platoon,
From frozen waste to desert dune.

We spent one lazy afternoon
In somewhere hot, I think Rangoon,
As house-guests of a rich tycoon.

We watched TV. There came a tune
On woodwind, piano and bassoon.
It introduced an old cartoon:
The Rabbit Who Tried To Catch The Moon.

I'll tell you about it...

Outside The Lucky Duck Saloon
In a cowboy town called Brigadoon
The rabbit who tried to catch the moon
Sat on the porch with Rick Racoon.

Inside, some tomcats played pontoon.
They howled. They spat in the spittoon.
Their paws hid claws as finely hewn
As pirate sword or ship's harpoon.

In fights, fur flew like that typhoon
Which blew through Chad and Cameroon.

The barman was a big baboon
Whose muscles made the toughest swoon.
With hide like steel, he seemed immune
To tooth, claw, bullet or harpoon.

The rabbit who tried to catch the moon
Sat silently with Rick Racoon.
Above them shone the summer moon
As round and bright as a gold doubloon.

The air was warm that night in June,
Like nest or den or silk cocoon;
The kind of night when street-cats croon,
The sort of sky that stars festoon –
A satin sheet, a deep lagoon
On which uncounted sparks are strewn.

The rabbit said to Rick Racoon:
"I'm going to catch myself that moon.
Its rare lamplight would be a boon.

I'll leap up there one night quite soon
When circumstance is opportune
And scoop it with a silver spoon."

That brought disdain from Rick Racoon:
"You nincompoop! You goofy goon!
You dunder-pated pantaloon!

A creature cannot own the moon.
It's not some kind of bright balloon,
Or grabable, like a macaroon.

It's huge and far, you poor buffoon.
It's dark and dry, just like a prune,
And so's your brain, you loony-tune."

"But this ain't life, we're in a cartoon,"
The rabbit replied to Rick Racoon...

Then: "Let's get moving, B Platoon!"
"Yes, sir!" "Yes, sir, Sergeant Calhoon!"
And we missed the end of our cartoon,
Never knew whether he caught his moon.

The sun sank low and glowed maroon.
The season then was mid-monsoon.
We marched through mud, but hummed that tune
Of woodwind, piano and bassoon...
While over us rose a marvellous moon.

The Grice Mice Device

Upon the concise
And extremely precise
Hand-written advice
Of one Gregory Grice
(Who was not very nice),
We placed a cheese slice
Inside the device
He'd designed to catch mice.

To quote Gregory Grice
Who was *not* very nice
(You've now heard that twice):

"One slice should suffice
To entice several mice.
They'll pay the full price
Once within my device
For, in less than a trice,
They'll be crushed in its vice
And dispatched to their mice paradise."

There...! I *told* you the man wasn't nice!

Cyril The Seafaring Squirrel

Admiral Squirrel,
Whose friends called him Cyril,
Once sailed his fleet up the Mersey

To shop in The Wirral
Where Admiral Squirrel
Purchased an Everton jersey.

Fishy Tongue-Twisting Questions
For The Sea-Slug

On the whole, would you say that a solo sole
Should enroll in a shoal of sole?

The slightly short-sighted light-shy sea-slug's slow shrug
Showed she was undecided.

Do the venomous antennae of anemones
Menace many of their eminent enemies?

The slightly short-sighted light-shy sea-slug's slow shrug
Still showed she was undecided.

Should shark-shadowed off-shore chic sleek sawfish
Seek sure safe shelter in sandy shallows?

The slightly short-sighted light-shy sea-slug's slow shrug
Still showed she was undecided.

Is its purpleness surplus to the purpose of a porpoise?
Is the shorter sort of shore-turtle surely not a tortoise?

The slightly short-sighted light-shy sea-slug's slow shrug
Still showed she was undecided.

Should we customarily trust crustaceans
When surly shellfish show such selfishness?

The slightly short-sighted light-shy sea-slug's slow shrug
Still showed she was undecided.

Other Children's Books By Nick Toczek

Me And My Poems (Caboodle '08)

Read Me Out Loud! (Macmillan '07)

Dragons! The Musical (Golden Apple '05)

Dragons! (Macmillan '05)

The Dog Ate My Bus Pass (Macmillan '04)

Sleeping Beauty's Dream (Golden Apple '03)

Kick It! (Macmillan '02)

Number Parade (LDA '02)

Can Anyone Be As Gloomy As Me? (Hodder '00, republished '05)

Toothpaste Trouble (Macmillan '02)

The Dragon Who Ate Our School (Macmillan '00)

Never Stare at a Grizzly Bear (Macmillan '00)

Join In... Or Else! (Macmillan '00)

Dragons Everywhere (Macmillan '97)

Dragons (Macmillan '95)